Developing Lite

NON-FICTION

READING AND WRITING
ACTIVITIES FOR THE LITERACY HOUR

year

5

Christine Moorcroft

Series consultant: Ray Barker

A & C BLACK

Contents

Writing composition

Acknowledgements
The author and publishers are grateful for permission to reproduce the following:
p. 9 text adapted from an article by Gavin Engelbrecht in *The Northern Echo*, Friday 18 May 2001; **p. 12** text adapted from an article on the *Darlington and Stockton Times* website, Friday 2 March 2001 (www.thisisthenortheast.co.uk/the_north_east/archive/2001/03/02/); **p. 25** text adapted from the Wookey Hole Cave website: www.wookey.co.uk; **p. 28** wild boars article adapted from *Metro* (Northeast) www.editorial@metronortheast.co.uk, Tuesday 12 June 2001; traffic article adapted from www.thisisgrimsby.co.uk; **p. 42** text adapted from *Egil's Saga*, in *The Icelandic Sagas*, translated by Magnus Magnusson (Folio Society, 1999).
The publishers apologise for the few instances in which they have been unable to make contact with the copyright holders, and would be grateful if they would contact the publishers.

Reprinted 2002
Published 2002 by
A & C Black Publishers Limited
37 Soho Square, London W1D 3QZ
www.acblack.com

ISBN 0-7136-6069-4

Copyright text © Christine Moorcroft, 2002
Copyright illustrations © Kirsty Wilson, 2002
Copyright cover illustration © Alison Dexter, 2002

The author and publishers would like to thank Ray Barker, Madeleine Madden, Julia Tappin and Sarah Vickers for their advice in producing this series of books.

A CIP catalogue record for this book is available from the British Library.

A & C Black uses paper produced with elemental chlorine-free pulp, harvested from managed sustainable forests.
Printed in Great Britain by Cromwell Press Ltd, Trowbridge, Wiltshire.

Introduction

Developing Literacy: Non-fiction is a series of seven photocopiable activity books for the Literacy Hour. Each book provides a range of non-fiction reading and writing activities, and supports the teaching of literacy skills at text, sentence and word levels.

The activities are designed to be carried out in the time allocated to independent work during the Literacy Hour. They incorporate strategies which encourage independent learning: for example, ways in which children can evaluate their own work or that of a partner.

The reading activities develop the children's study and research skills (reading for a purpose, understanding and interpreting, and making use of what they have read) and provide models on which they can base their own writing.

The writing activities concentrate on the purpose of a text, the audience for whom it is written and the context in which it is to be read, and encourage the children to be aware of these considerations when they write.

The activities in **Year 5** reinforce word, text and sentence-level skills and encourage the children to:

- identify the features of recounted texts, such as sports reports, and use these features in their own recounts;

- read, follow, evaluate and write instructions (and evaluate their own writing);

- develop skills in preparing for research quickly by reviewing what they already know, what they need to find out, the available sources of information (appraising them to check which are the most useful) and presenting their notes from different sources in an organised format;

- develop skills in scanning a printed or electronic text to find out what it is about, skimming it to find useful headings, phrases or sentences and using these as tools for summarising it;

- monitor their own understanding of a text and develop strategies to make sense of difficult texts;

- develop skills in marking extracts in a way which helps them to make notes;

- write notes quickly and efficiently in a way which is suitable for their purpose, and fill out notes to produce connected prose;

- learn how writers record sources, and begin to do so in their own writing;

- understand how paragraphs are used in organising and sequencing information;

- read, write and evaluate letters for different audiences and purposes;

- develop an awareness of the ways in which language can be used to influence opinion, and write persuasive texts in the form of letters, commentaries, arguments and advertisements;

- evaluate and edit their own writing.

The National Literacy Strategy and non-fiction

The National Literacy Strategy *Framework for Teaching* encourages teachers to use all kinds of non-fiction texts, both printed and electronic: for example, instructions (such as rules, recipes and directions); reports and articles from newspapers and magazines giving facts, information, explanations and opinions; information books and CD-ROMs giving facts and explanations; advertisements from different media; leaflets and flyers; letters; and discussion texts such as editorials and reviews.

Links to other subjects

The children can use their literacy skills to further their learning in other subjects, through the reading of shared texts or guided reading during the Literacy Hour and by using and developing their research skills at other times. During the Literacy Hour, the children can write about what they have learned in other subjects and learn how to select the best methods for their writing.

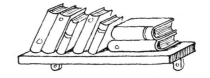

Using non-fiction in the Literacy Hour

While the activities in this book focus on the independent part of the Literacy Hour, the notes on pages 6 to 8 and at the foot of each activity page suggest a variety of ways you can introduce non-fiction reading and writing, present whole-class activities and use the plenary session to conclude the lesson. The ideas support the following strategies:

- **demonstrating** or modelling the way in which an experienced reader and writer tackles a skill or an approach to reading or writing, by 'thinking aloud' about what you are doing;

- **sharing** an activity: the teacher or other adult (as the expert) takes responsibility for the difficult parts of the activity, while the learners take responsibility for the easier parts. The learners then gradually take over some of the more difficult parts. This bridges the gap between demonstration and independent work;

- **supporting** an activity, in which the children undertake the activity independently, with the teacher (or other adult) monitoring and being ready to offer support when necessary. This avoids the difficulties which arise when the teacher moves from demonstration or modelling to asking the children to work independently.

Children will benefit from learning the following strategies to help them read and write non-fiction:

- **predicting** (suggesting what information a book or page might provide, and how they can tell);

- **clarifying** (working out ways in which to understand new or difficult words and ideas);

- **questioning** (saying what questions the text raises and what it makes them want to find out);

- **summarising** (saying in a limited number of words what the text is about and what it tells them).

The activities in this book support the following stages of the children's interactions with text:

- **bringing to mind what they already know** about the subject (for example, by making flow-charts, diagrams and lists);

- **deciding what they want to find out** (for example, by writing questions);

- **deciding where to find the information they need** (for example, information books, electronic texts, people and websites);

- **learning the best ways in which to use the source** (from the teacher or other adult, who models the use of the source);

- **developing strategies to help them understand the text** (for example, marking difficult words or passages, and re-phrasing or transferring information from prose to charts or from diagrams to prose);

- **recording information** (using charts and note-making strategies such as abbreviation);

- **evaluating the information** (for example, evaluating the validity of the source or comparing information from different sources, and separating facts from opinions);

- **communicating information** (considering the audience, purpose and context of the text to be written and their effects on language and layout).

Extension activities

Most of the activity sheets end with a challenge (**Now try this!**) which reinforces and extends the children's learning and provides the teacher with an opportunity for assessment. These more challenging activities might be appropriate for only a few children; it is not expected that the whole class should complete them. For most of the extension activities, the children will need a notebook or a separate sheet of paper.

Organisation

The activities require very few resources besides scissors, glue, word-banks and a range of dictionaries. Other materials are specified in the teachers' notes on the activity pages.

Notes on the activities

The notes below expand upon those which are provided at the foot of each activity page. They give ideas and suggestions for making the most of the activity sheet, including suggestions for the whole-class introduction, the plenary session or for follow-up work using an adapted version of the activity sheet. To help teachers select appropriate learning experiences for their pupils, the activities are grouped into sections, but the pages need not be presented in the order in which they appear in the book, unless otherwise stated.

Reading comprehension

The activities in this section reinforce the children's word-level and sentence-level skills and develop their ability to read, use and understand the structure and language style of newspaper and magazine reports, instructions, non-chronological reports, information books, explanatory, discursive and promotional texts (including advertisements), editorials and various electronic texts. The activities encourage the children to plan their work by bringing to mind what they already know, formulating questions and then locating the answers in non-fiction texts. They help the children to distinguish between information and opinion and to use the features of non-fiction texts to find information. The children learn how to appraise information texts, instructions and explanations to decide how well they will provide the information they want, to scan the texts to find that information and to skim-read before deciding which parts to annotate and make notes from. They develop skills in summarising texts and organising notes from different sources.

News splash (page 9). This activity increases the children's understanding of the structure and features of newspaper reports. They could first read other newspaper reports about events and notice their structure. Many newspaper reports present a story so that it 'unfolds': some information is given in the introductory paragraph to orientate the reader, but details are omitted, leading the reader to the next paragraph. Sentences and paragraphs are linked with interesting connectives. The extension activity focuses on the way in which the final paragraph concludes the story and leaves the reader with something to think about (how the other sponsors are going to react).

Make a whizz-bang (page 10). This activity encourages the children to follow instructions carefully and then to evaluate them, noticing the features which made them easy to follow.

Spot the difference (page 11). This activity focuses on the differences between formal and informal language. Teachers could also draw attention to the way in which each type of text addresses the reader, noting that informal writing speaks directly to the reader and uses active and imperative forms of verbs, whereas formal writing addresses the reader indirectly and uses the passive form of verbs and a more sophisticated vocabulary.

A game of two halves (page 12). In this activity the children develop their understanding of how a recount is structured. They could try to identify the opening paragraph from its first sentence. Ask them how they can tell that it comes before the other paragraphs. They should be able to complete the ordering in a similar way.

A jigsaw of clauses (page 13). This activity focuses on the structure of complex sentences. The children learn to link a subordinate clause (one which depends on the main clause for sense) to a main clause (the most important clause in the sentence – the clause on which the others depend for sense).

Pigs might fly! (page 14). This activity explains hypothetical language (the language of 'ifs' and 'mights') and how it is used. The questions are open-ended, but the following are example answers: 1. If you were to go to the Moon, perhaps you would see where moonbeams begin; 2. Pigs might fly if they grew wings; 3. If I ruled the world I would bring back the dinosaurs; 4. If there is water there, there could be life on Mars; 5. If I had a magic wand maybe I could make everyone friends; 6. If everyone in the world had a computer we could all send messages to each other; 7. I would be very surprised if an owl should say 'Good morning'; 8. If our heads were turned back-to-front we would need to carry a mirror.

Let me explain (page 15). This activity focuses on the features of explanatory texts: technical language, hypothetical language, logical connectives, passive verbs and complex sentences. The children could also use the page to help them analyse other explanations. As an additional extension activity, they could make a glossary of the technical words in the passage.

The information seekers (page 16). This activity models how to prepare for reading for information, by calling to mind what the reader already knows about a topic and what he or she needs to find out or check. The children can be encouraged to use the same procedure when they research new topics for themselves.

Mr Know-it-All (page 17). This activity helps the children to use information texts efficiently. Different groups of children could use different sources to answer the same question, and compare which was the most efficient.

Technically tricky (page 18). This activity develops the children's skills in monitoring their understanding of what they read. It encourages them, when they are reading closely for detailed information, to stop and think about the meaning of each sentence and to develop strategies for making sense of the difficult parts.

A-tishoo! (page 19). This activity encourages the children to consider the way in which the presentation of information is affected by the purpose of a text. It also revises the features of different types of non-fiction texts. They should notice person, tense, forms of verbs (for example, imperative), voice (active or passive) and style of language (personal or impersonal, formal or informal). **Answers**: 1) explanation, 2) non-chronological report, 3) recount, 4) instructions, 5) advertisement. The extension activity develops skills in making notes about information from different sources, and in organising notes.

Writers' records (page 20). This activity develops the children's appreciation of the need to record sources of information, both so that they can return to them if necessary and so that their readers can read them for themselves. The sources are usually recorded in alphabetical order, either by title or author's family name.

Speedy notes (page 21). This encourages the children to make notes quickly by using abbreviations which are meaningful when they return to their notes and by omitting unnecessary words.

In your own words: a recount and **In your own words: persuasion** (pages 22–23). These activities provide structures to help the children think about the purpose of their notes and the most helpful format for them (with regard to what they will write later). The flow-chart on page 22 matches the chronological structure of a recount. The 'star chart' on page 23 matches the way in which a persuasive text is structured.

I must protest! (page 24). This activity develops the children's awareness of the ways in which writers can gain the reader's attention, give an impression of authority and affect the reader's opinions. The children could classify a variety of letters to newspapers according to their purpose: for example, to inform, protest, complain or persuade.

www.information.com (page 25). This activity encourages the children to notice the way in which information is presented and the purpose of the information. The website from which the text is taken is designed to inform people about the Wookey Hole Cave Centre and to encourage them to visit it. The children could re-write the text, giving only facts, and compare their own version with the original.

The whole truth? 1 and 2 (pages 26–27). These pages show the children that some texts present information in a way which persuades people to buy something, do something or go somewhere. A display of advertisements could be made, with parts of the texts labelled to show which devices are being used.

Sum it up (page 28). This activity develops the children's skills in summarising, first to list the main points of the text and then to say, briefly, what it is about. Before they begin the activity, the children could read headlines and summaries of news reports, and the reports themselves, on local news websites.

Writing composition

These activities develop the children's skills in making notes in a way which supports their writing for different purposes. There are structures which help the children to organise their writing for different purposes and to use appropriate styles of language: for example, writing in the style of newspaper articles, and writing instructions, rules, persuasive letters, arguments and commentaries. The children also learn to adapt their writing for different audiences, using either personal or impersonal language.

Write a recount (page 29). This activity provides a framework which helps the children to write their notes in the correct sequence. The flow-chart encourages chronological writing, linking one event to the next. The page can be used to structure recounts in other subjects.

Be a sports reporter (page 30). This activity helps the children to use the structure and key features of a newspaper sports report in their own writing. In converting information in note-form and on charts to prose, the children have to interpret the information; this helps them to re-write it in their own words.

From friend to stranger (page 31). In this activity the children convert personal to impersonal writing. They could first identify any parts which should be deleted because they were originally addressed to a specific person.

Write a recipe and **Scriptwriter** (pages 32–33). These require the children to interpret information presented in the form of labelled and annotated diagrams, and to convert it into prose. On page 33 they need to take extra care to make their language clear, since the listener cannot see the diagrams. In the extension activity they should make notes about parts where the listener was unsure what to do, and think of ways to clarify them.

Rule writer (page 34). This page provides a structure which lets the children write the rules for a game and then try out and evaluate instructions written by others. The activity could be introduced by inviting a child to come to the front and answer questions about a game he or she knows well: for example, 'What is it called?' 'What equipment do you need?' 'What is the playing area like?' and 'How does the game end?' An enlarged copy of the activity sheet could be completed using the information given by the child in answer to the questions.

Short and sweet: 1 and 2 (pages 35–36). These pages provide practice in recognising standard abbreviations. The children learn abbreviations which can be used in notes both for themselves and for others. The foreign sources are all Latin except for *khilioi* (thousand), which is Greek.

Text it (page 37). This activity gives examples of the ways in which words can be shortened by using conventional abbreviations or by omitting vowels. The children could use text messaging abbreviations for speed when making notes.

Be persuasive: 1 and 2 (pages 38–39). These pages focus on the structure and language of persuasive writing. The format provided on page 38 encourages the children to think of the main ideas in the point they are making and to support each one with evidence. The activities could be introduced after the children have expressed points of view on a topic orally and have been asked to justify their opinions.

Five steps for taking notes (page 40). This activity allows the children to focus on the process and purpose of taking notes. Once they have completed the activity, they could keep a copy of it in a place where it can easily be found for reference.

Calendar notes (page 41). This requires the children to understand what they read and to monitor their own understanding (see also page 18). They transfer the information from the text to the calendar. They could make use of a calendar format for recording other information relating to dates which need to be checked at a glance.

Family tree notes (page 42). Like the previous activity, this requires the children to understand what they read and to monitor their own understanding (see also page 18). They transfer the information from the text to the family tree. The children will appreciate why the people's names sound so unusual if they know that *Egil's Saga* is about people who lived in Iceland in the tenth century. The children could also construct their own family trees, and others to show relationships between people in religious texts such as the Bible and the Hindu scriptures. This process will help them to make sense of complex relationships in the texts.

Notes to text (page 43). This develops the children's skills in filling out notes into connected prose. In doing so, they also learn about the ways in which notes can be written both for speed and so that they suit their purpose.

From notes to report (page 44). This activity provides a structure which the children could use (with different headings) for their own notes for a non-chronological report. It also provides a structure for the writing of a non-chronological report, with hints to help the children decide what to write. They could compare the connectives used in a non-chronological report with those used in a recount, a commentary and an argument.

Change the audience (page 45). This activity encourages the children to monitor their own understanding of a text by asking them to re-write it in a different way. They should look up any words they do not understand in order to re-write the text more simply. When the children edit their first drafts, encourage them to check that they have not made the new text much longer than the original. Ask them whether any parts can be taken out or shortened.

Make it formal (page 46). This activity asks the children to focus on the differences between formal and informal language: the words used, the structure of the sentences, the type of language (a direct, personal style or an indirect, impersonal style) and the use of subjunctives and the passive form of verbs.

Write a commentary (page 47). This activity provides a format to help the children organise their notes for a commentary. It encourages them to check the evidence they use to support their point of view.

Present an argument (page 48). In this activity the children develop their skills in constructing an argument. They are required to think of points that other people might raise against their argument, and to think of counter-arguments. In writing each point they wish to make on separate cards, which are kept apart from the cards containing points which might be raised against the argument, the children learn to write in a way which suits the audience, purpose and context.

News splash

- **Read the newspaper report.**

A news report is a recount. It is mainly written in the past tense.

A dear do as daughter swims off with pounds

When Alison Blair was asked by her eleven-year-old daughter, Holly, to sponsor a fund-raising swim she thought nothing of offering her £1 for every length. After all, she thought, it wouldn't come to more than a few pounds.

But she had not counted on her daughter's steely determination. She watched with a sinking feeling as Holly completed length after length, reaching an amazing total of 123 lengths of the 25-metre swimming pool!

Alison, of Gosforth, Newcastle, said last night: 'I couldn't believe my eyes. I thought of changing the sponsor form, but that wouldn't have been fair. It is for such a good cause – and Holly deserves it.'

Holly was one of seven young swimmers at the Newcastle City baths who swam a total of 536 lengths in aid of St Oswald's Hospice.

Friends and neighbours also sponsored Holly, but the Blairs have yet to work out how much she is owed.

The Blairs are preparing themselves for the reactions.

- **Describe how the introductory paragraph sets the scene.**
- **Make a chart to show how the recount lists the events in the story.**

What is the story about? What does it make you think might happen? How?

Paragraph	Information	Connectives
1		

Now try this!

- **What does the final paragraph make you think will happen next?**

Teachers' note You could first write the headline on the board and ask the children to predict what the report will be about. They could check their predictions later. Read the report together and ask the children to notice in which tense the text is written. The chart-making activity emphasises that the recount does not give the events in the order in which they happened.

Developing Literacy
Non-fiction Year 5
© A & C Black 2002

Make a whizz-bang

- **Read the instructions.**
- **Make a whizz-bang.**

> Your teacher might not want you to test the whizz-bang during lessons!

A whizz-bang

You need:

- a piece of stiff card at least 36 cm × 21 cm (cereal box card works well)
- a piece of strong paper at least 22 cm × 13 cm
- sticky tape
- a ruler
- scissors
- a pencil

1. Cut out a piece of card like this:

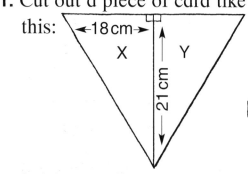

←18 cm→
X   Y
21 cm

Label it X and Y.

2. Cut out a piece of paper like this:

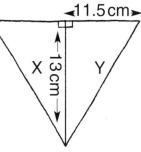

←11.5 cm→
X 13 cm Y

Label it X and Y.

3. Fasten X to X and Y to Y with sticky tape:

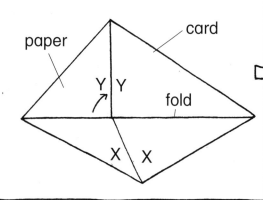

paper   card
Y Y
fold
X X

4. Fold the card and paper shape flat:

card fold
paper   X

(Y cannot be seen. It is on the back.)

5. Push the paper inside the card and fold it.

paper inside   X   card

Now try this!

- **List the features which helped you to follow the instructions.**

> Say how they helped.

Teachers' note As the children follow the instructions, they could make notes of anything they find difficult and anything which makes the instructions easy to follow, including the use of pictures and diagrams and the way in which they are labelled.

Developing Literacy Non-fiction Year 5 © A & C Black 2002

Spot the difference

• **Read the** formal **and** informal **texts.**

Formal

Guests wishing to use the Leisure Club facilities are requested to:
• deposit their room key at the reception desk;
• sign the visitors' book and enter their time of arrival.
• Towels are provided for use in the Leisure Club.
• Swimwear and toiletries may be purchased from the reception staff.
• Guests are requested to sign the visitors' book and enter their time of leaving.

Informal

• If you want to use our Leisure Club, just hand in your room key at the reception desk.
• As you go in, please sign your name and write the time in the visitors' book.
• No need to bring a towel; you can borrow one while you're using the club.
• You can buy swimwear and toiletries at the desk.
• Don't forget to sign the visitors' book and write the time when you leave.

• **Copy and complete the chart to show the differences.**

	Formal text	Informal text
Verb form		
Person		
How guests are addressed		
Different words and phrases with the same meaning	Guests wishing deposit	If you want to hand in
Other differences		

• **Choose a different formal text. Re-write it, making it informal.**

Now try this!

Teachers' note You could introduce the activity by reading other formal and informal texts with the children and asking them to classify them as 'formal' or 'informal'. Ask them to explain their classifications, and introduce or revise the language with which to do this. Provide a selection of formal texts for the extension activity.

Developing Literacy
Non-fiction Year 5
© A & C Black 2002

A game of two halves

- **Put the paragraphs in the correct order.**
- **Underline the connective words and phrases.**

DRAW TAKES DURHAM LADIES INTO SEMI-FINALS

Durham City Ladies 3 ... Newton Aycliffe Ladies 3

The second half was an open game with chances falling to both teams. Sarah Alexander gave Newton Aycliffe hope when she scored from a long-range free-kick.

Their 6–2 win in the first leg gave Durham a four-goal cushion as they entered the second leg, which ended in a 3–3 draw, the match having gone ahead following a morning pitch inspection.

With fewer than ten minutes remaining Nicky Duckling brought the score to 3–2, and Durham suddenly found themselves defending frantically. They had to settle for a draw when Kim O'Connor scored a great goal from outside the box with the last kick of the game.

Durham City have reached the semi-finals of the Northern League Second Division Cup with a 9–5 aggregate win over Newton Aycliffe.

Durham will play Penrith over two legs in the semi-final.

Durham raced into a 3–0 lead within the first 30 minutes. The first goal came after Gemma Charlton had been brought down in the box, Claire Turner converting the penalty. Amanda Smith made some great runs down the right and Helen Richardson converted one of Smith's crosses for a second. Richardson quickly scored again, blasting home a cross from the left, this time from Magda Carr. Just before the break Durham's Julie Campbell conceded a penalty; however, the spot-kick was missed.

- **Re-write the report, using different connective words and phrases.**

Keep the meaning the same.

Teachers' note The children should first have read other sports reports (for example, those in newspapers) and noticed the way in which the sentences and paragraphs in them are linked chronologically (this might sometimes involve 'flashbacks' to earlier events). Ask them to list the 'time connectives' which are used.

Developing Literacy
Non-fiction Year 5
© A & C Black 2002

A jigsaw of clauses

A complex sentence has:

a main clause

at least one subordinate clause

The sense of the subordinate clause depends on the main clause.

The magic worked only if the witch wore blue tights.

- **Link the clauses on the jigsaw pieces in any way you like to make complex sentences.**
- **Write on the chart.**

Useful connectives

as long as	only
because	only when
for fear that	so that
if	to
in case	when

a lazy dragon licked its lips

Mary made her way to the Moon

monsters munch mustard

the aliens were following her

it saw the red seaweed

they can breathe fire

The main clause is the most important one.

Main clause	Connective	Subordinate clause

Now try this!

- **Write six clauses on pieces of card.**
- **Swap them with a friend.**
- **Make the clauses into complex sentences.**

Join your friend's clauses with logical connectives.

Examples: he eats spinach   she mixes spells
make him strong   cause trouble

Teachers' note It is useful first to revise simple sentences (one clause: The girl shouted) and compound sentences (two main clauses which each make sense without the other: The girl shouted but the boy whispered). Revise complex sentences (a main, and at least one subordinate, clause: The girl shouted that she would not come out).

**Developing Literacy
Non-fiction Year 5
© A & C Black 2002**

Pigs might fly!

Hypothetical language **is about things which <u>might</u> happen.**

If money grew on trees
he would plant a forest.

• **Make up hypothetical sentences
using the clauses below.**

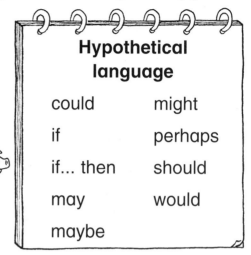

You can use the
clause either to begin
or end the sentence.

**Hypothetical
language**

could	might
if	perhaps
if... then	should
may	would
maybe	

1. if you were to
go to the Moon

2. pigs might fly

3. if I ruled
the world

4. there could be
life on Mars

5. if I had a
magic wand

6. if everyone in the
world had a computer

7. if an owl should say
'Good morning'

8. we would need to
carry a mirror

1. _If you were to go to the Moon perhaps
you would see_

2. _____

3. _____

4. _____

5. _____

6. _____

7. _____

8. _____

Now
try
this!

• **Write six more sentences using
hypothetical language.**

Teachers' note It is useful to point out that hypothetical language is not as complicated as it sounds; it is the language used when people guess, predict, suggest ideas or wonder.

**Developing Literacy
Non-fiction Year 5
© A & C Black 2002**

Let me explain

- ## Read the explanation and look at the diagrams.

How we see colours

Light is made up of all the colours of the spectrum. These colours can be seen in a rainbow.

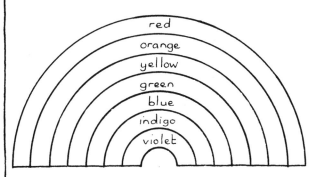

Paints and all coloured things contain pigments. If something is coloured blue, it is because its pigments absorb all except the blue light. The blue light is not absorbed; it is reflected, and so that is the colour we see.

If something is white, its pigments do not absorb any of the light. They reflect all the colours of the light; because this mixture of all colours of light makes white, we see white.

If something is black, its pigments absorb all the light which hits them. No light is reflected, and so we see black, which is an absence of light.

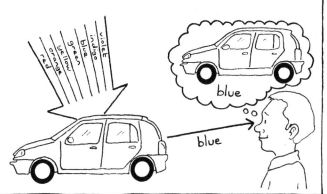

- ## Look for the special features of explanations. Copy and complete the chart.

Give examples.

Features of explanations				
Technical language	**Hypothetical language**	**Logical connectives**	**Passive verbs**	**Diagrams**
spectrum	If something is...			

Now try this!

Explanations often use complex sentences.
- ## Give two examples from the explanation.

A complex sentence has a main clause and at least one subordinate clause.

Teachers' note The children should first have completed page 13 (and, if they undertake the extension activity, page 14). You might need to revise the passive form of verbs. The children could complete a similar analysis of other explanatory texts.

**Developing Literacy
Non-fiction Year 5
© A & C Black 2002**

The information seekers

These children are learning about the Picts.

- **Read what they say.**
- **Write some questions to help them with their research.**

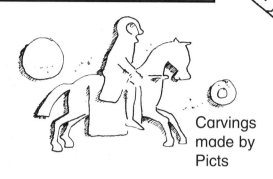

Carvings made by Picts

I am finding out about when and where the Picts lived. I know they lived in Britain a long time ago.

Between which years did the Picts live in Britain?

Where in Britain did they live?

I am finding out about the religion of the Picts. I know they were pagans.

I am finding out about stones carved by the Picts. I have heard of the Aberlemno Stone.

I am finding out about the battles fought by the Picts. I know that one was called the Battle of Dunnichen.

I am finding out about the clothing and any jewellery worn by the Picts. I know that 'Picts' means 'painted people'.

Now try this!

- **Write five paragraphs about a new topic you are studying.**

Remember to organise what you write into separate sections.

Teachers' note Before the children begin the activity, it will be useful to model how to decide which questions will help the person looking for information (as in the example given).

**Developing Literacy
Non-fiction Year 5
© A & C Black 2002**

Mr Know-it-All

Know-it-All's Information Service

Assistant wanted

Scan the index.

Use information texts.

Scan the contents page or opening page.

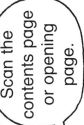
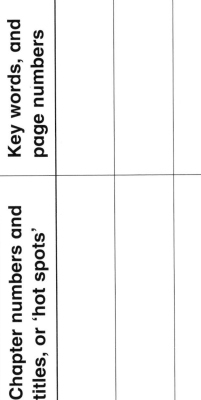
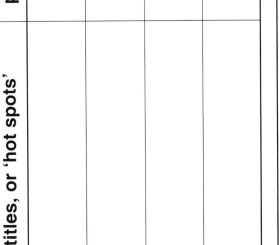

Mr Know-it-All is an information finder. He tells people where they can find the information they want.

- You are going to be Mr Know-it-All's assistant.
- Complete the information form for a customer.

Choose the best text you can find.

Question	Text: title, author and publisher	Chapter numbers and titles, or 'hot spots'	Key words, and page numbers
How do plants make their food?			
What is soil made of?			
Where is the source of the River Mersey?			
Why do stars twinkle?			

- Write new questions on a blank copy of the form.
- Give it to a friend to complete.

Now try this!

Teachers' note Model how to approach each question on the form: the children first need to make a note of what they already know about the topic of the question, since this will help them to select appropriate texts (for example, 'Plants use sunlight to make their food from gases in the air'). They should search both printed and electronic texts.

Developing Literacy
Non-fiction Year 5
© A & C Black 2002

Technically tricky

Explanations often contain technical **words which might be difficult to understand.**

Use a dictionary.

- **Read the passage. Underline any technical words.**

Why do we get scabs on cuts?

The skin covers the internal parts of the body to protect them. A cut is a hole in the skin through which germs can get in and blood can get out.

Blood contains materials which form clots when air reaches it; the clots make the blood thicker and so it flows more slowly from the cut.

White blood cells swarm into the cut from the blood vessels around it. They break down dirt and germs.

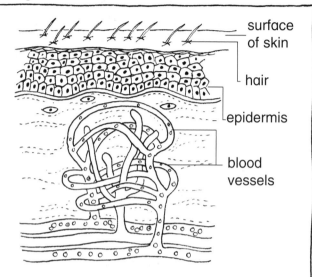

surface of skin
hair
epidermis
blood vessels

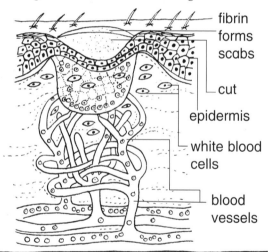

fibrin forms scabs
cut
epidermis
white blood cells
blood vessels

Small blood cells called platelets form a material called fibrin. Fibrin joins up the gap in the skin made by the cut. It seals any damaged blood vessels.

The scab is made of hardened fibrin and debris from the injured skin. It protects the skin and tissue beneath it while the cells in the epidermis multiply to join up the gap. The scab falls off once the skin is healed.

- **Copy and complete the chart. It will help you to work out the meanings of the technical words.**

See how many meanings you can work out before you look them up.

| Word | How to find the meaning | | | |
	From the diagrams	From the text	From other words with similar meanings	From a dictionary
cell	I can see what it looks like	blood contains cells	A small room, so it might be something small	A tiny part of a living thing

Teachers' note Introduce the activity by modelling how to read a technical explanation. Read a sentence aloud and ask the children if they know what it means. What makes it difficult to understand? Help them to work out the meanings of words, where possible, by considering any similarities they have with other words. Model how to select appropriate reference texts in which to look up meanings.

Developing Literacy
Non-fiction Year 5
© A & C Black 2002

A-tishoo!

- **Read the passages. What are they about?** _____

- **Match each passage to a text-type. Write the letter in the circle.**

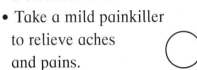

Text-types

a. advertisement

b. explanation

c. instructions

d. non-chronological report

e. recount

1. Once the cold virus has entered the body, the body's natural defences begin to work. These defences cause the symptoms of a cold: extra mucus is produced, causing a runny, or even blocked, nose.

2. Adults have an average of two to four colds per year, and young children have an average of six to eight. In general, people usually have colds between September and May.

3. On the bus to school he was sitting beside a woman who coughed and sneezed without once using a handkerchief. Some of the germs that she spread must have found their way into his nose. Within a couple of days he had a runny nose.

4.
- Drink plenty of liquid.
- Use vapour rubs on your chest to clear a blocked nose.
- Take a mild painkiller to relieve aches and pains.

5. Wacko zaps colds! New improved formula. Scientifically tested. New flavours: cherry cheer and blackcurrant burst.

- **Complete the chart.**

Passage	Purpose	Where it might be from
1	to explain	
2		
3		
4		
5		

- **Make a chart to record the main points from the passage.**

Now try this!

Add other headings to the chart.

How you catch a cold	What happens in your body	How to treat a cold

Teachers' note You could begin by revising the features of the different types of texts listed on the notepad: for example, tense, verb form, person and type of language. Discuss the purposes of different text-types and where they might be found. The children could carry out a similar analysis to the one on the activity sheet using texts on a different topic.

Developing Literacy
Non-fiction Year 5
© A & C Black 2002

Writers' records

Writers of information books usually list the texts they used in their research.

They list the texts under headings such as these:

Bibliography

References

Further reading

Other books you could read

• Look at some information books in your class or school library.

• Fill in the chart to show how the authors record the [sources] they used.

Title and author of book	How the author recorded his or her sources		
	Title of list (e.g. Bibliography)	Where in the book? Inside back cover? Last page?	Information given about sources (e.g. author, date)	Order of sources (e.g. alphabetical by author)

• Make a chart to record details about information books you have used in your research.

Now try this!

Title	Author	Publisher	Date published

Teachers' note The children need access to information books in the class or school library. Ask them to notice the order in which the sources are recorded (for example, alphabetical by author or book title), and the order in which information about them is presented. Discuss what each piece of information refers to, for example, publisher and date of publication.

Developing Literacy
Non-fiction Year 5
© A & C Black 2002

Speedy notes

You can speed up your note-making by using abbreviations and by missing out unimportant words.

- **Write notes about what the people say, using abbreviations. Complete the key.**

I'd like tomato soup please, with a wholemeal roll, followed by chicken and roast potatoes with broccoli and cauliflower. I'd also like a glass of orange juice.

I tom sp

Go straight on to the end of Dog Lane. Turn left at the roundabout and continue until you reach the library. Take the first right; that is Chain Avenue. The first building on the right is the leisure centre.

My name is William Grey. I live at 72 West High Street in Birmingham. My postcode is B83 7OP.

Key to abbreviations

Avenue
broccoli
building
cauliflower
centre
chicken
continue
first
juice
Lane
left
leisure
library
orange
potatoes
right
roundabout
sp   soup
straight on
Street
tom   tomato
until
West
wholemeal

Now try this!

- **Exchange notes with a friend.**
- **Cover the passages. Then re-write them using your notes.**

You could cover the passages with stickers.

Teachers' note The children could first use dictionaries to find out about standard abbreviations. Discuss the symbols, such as arrows, which can replace words for directions, and the words which can be omitted for brevity. See also pages 35–37.

Developing Literacy
Non-fiction Year 5
© A & C Black 2002

In your own words: a recount

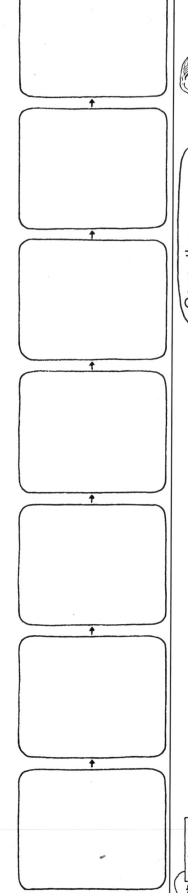

- **Read the passage. On the flow-chart, make notes of the main points.**

The wreck of the *Forfarshire*

On Wednesday 5 September 1838 a steamship named the *Forfarshire* set off from Hull to Dundee, carrying 63 passengers, its crew and cargo.

The next morning the ship's boiler began to leak. By now the ship was just north of the Farne Islands and a storm was brewing.

At one o'clock on the Friday morning the engine stopped; the *Forfarshire* began to drift. Suddenly there was a great crash as the ship struck Great Harcar rock.

Meanwhile, at the nearby Longstone lighthouse, a young woman was awoken by the storm. Her name was Grace Darling; her father, William, was the lighthouse keeper. She looked out to sea and spotted the ship.

They thought the sea was too rough for the Sunderland lifeboat crew on shore to set out, so together Grace and William Darling launched their own boat. It was a struggle, but they finally made it to the rocks. They found nine survivors and three dead – but the boat could carry only seven people. With the help of three of the men, William rowed back to the lighthouse with Grace and an injured woman, and then returned for the others.

Not long afterwards the Sunderland lifeboat crew reached the rock but found only the dead passengers. They went on to the lighthouse for shelter. To their astonishment they found it crowded with people!

- **Re-write the recount using only your notes.**

Cover the passage so you cannot see it.

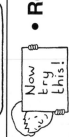

Now try this!

Developing Literacy
Non-fiction Year 5
© A & C Black 2002

Teachers' note You could introduce the activity by reading out another short recount, such as a newspaper story, and then asking the children to re-tell it in their own words. Point out the need for making notes to remember the main points, and discuss the most helpful ways of organising their notes for a recount (in the correct order).

In your own words: persuasion

- **Read the passage.**

There are many good reasons for objecting to having a mobile phone mast put up in the school grounds. Many scientific reports have shown that harmful radiation comes from mobile phone masts. We do not yet know what this radiation can do to people. It is thought that children are more likely to be affected than adults. So a school is the worst possible place to put a mast.

In addition to the health risk, we should think about what the masts look like: they are usually taller than the surrounding buildings and of an ugly appearance.

A new mast might make it possible for mobile phones using the Bignet system to work in the area, but other networks (such as Littlenet) work perfectly well here already. Why harm our environment for the convenience of one small group of people?

In addition to the problems already mentioned, the village is a conservation area. A mobile phone mast would alter the appearance of the area in a way that should not be allowed.

A mobile phone mast would not benefit the local people in any way. People's health and the well-being of the local environment are much more important than making money for big businesses.

- **Make notes on the 'star chart' about the main points.**

Write the main points in the boxes and the evidence on the lines.

☆ Phone mast would be a health risk

☆

☆

☆

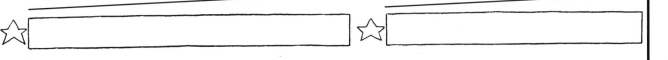

Now try this!

- **Re-write the persuasive text using only your notes.**

Teachers' note It will be useful to discuss the purpose of persuasive texts, how they are structured and how each point made should be supported by evidence or reasoning. You could also discuss the connectives used to link the points (logical connectives, such as 'because', 'in addition to', 'therefore' and 'thus'). Encourage the children to compare their re-written text with the original.

**Developing Literacy
Non-fiction Year 5
© A & C Black 2002**

I must protest!

- **Read the letters. Consider how they use language.**

Dear Editor,
It is a waste of public money to pull down the statue in City Square. The sculpture of the giant yellow sheep was put there only two years ago at great expense. It has become a feature of the city. My friends and I adore it. The complaints of a few grumblers with no sense of humour are not a good enough reason for pulling it down. I say Keep the Sheep!
Yours sincerely,
Ava Laff (aged 10),
2 Ticklerib Street

Dear Editor,
Let's use common sense! There is no point in putting up signs banning dogs from Central Park. Dogs accompanied by their owners and kept on a lead are no problem. It's strays that wander in that do the damage – and they can't read the signs! Take the signs down, I say.
Yours truly,
Ima Beagle,
7 Kennel Lane

Dear Editor,
Isn't it obvious? Of course North Road Station must be re-opened. A good rail link would reduce the disgraceful amount of traffic on the road. Less traffic would mean less air pollution – surely a vital consideration for an area which has the most polluted air in the country.
Yours,
Colonel C Blimp, Back-of-Beyond,
Out Lane

Dear Editor,
Has the world gone mad?. Whatever next? A fruit and vegetable grower has produced cube-shaped melons! Why? For no better reason than to stop them rolling around on the shelf of the fridge! What next? Cubic apples? Rectangular stacking pineapples? Or even pyramid-shaped figs, all the same size, so that they pack neatly in boxes?
Yours truly,
Gita Grip,
The Orchard,
Leafy Lane

- **Copy and complete the chart.**

Words and phrases used to:		
gain attention	give an impression of authority	change people's opinions

---

Teachers' note Read the first letter with the children and discuss the way in which the writer's opinion is made clear at the outset. Discuss examples of exaggeration, extremes and superlatives: for example, 'a few grumblers', 'adore', 'at great expense', 'no sense of humour'.

Developing Literacy
Non-fiction Year 5
© A & C Black 2002

www.information.com

- **Read this text from a website. Underline the information. Circle the words and phrases which give opinions.**

www.TheMagicalMirrorMaze.com

Showmen have always used mirrors to create glitter and illusion. The old distorting mirrors are as popular as ever and still raise a giggle from passing crowds. The Magical Mirror Maze is a modern version of the old-fashioned mirror show.

More than forty mirrors, each eight feet high and set at precise 60° angles, create the impression of a huge colourful crypt with a vaulted ceiling; the many twists and turns appear to be long straight passages going in all directions – until you try to walk along one!

The musical fountain at the end of the maze is reflected through the maze of mirrors. As you find your way through the maze, the fountain sometimes disappears from view only to reappear somewhere else.

The water in the multi-jet fountain dances to the music; the height and the mixture of the water plumes are controlled by changes of tone in the music, using state-of-the-art technology. Water valves open in time with the music and the shimmering coloured lights which surround the fountain.

- **Copy and complete the chart.**

Information	List the facts.	Opinion	List words and phrases which create effects.
Each mirror is eight feet high.		Old mirrors as popular as ever.	

Now try this!

- **Write a summary of the facts in the text.**
- **Write a summary of the opinions in the text.**

Write one sentence for each summary.

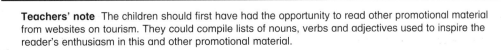

Teachers' note The children should first have had the opportunity to read other promotional material from websites on tourism. They could compile lists of nouns, verbs and adjectives used to inspire the reader's enthusiasm in this and other promotional material.

**Developing Literacy
Non-fiction Year 5
© A & C Black 2002**

The whole truth? 1

- **Read the extracts from advertisements.**
- **Look for:**

half-truth	deliberate use of ambiguity
bias	opinions disguised as facts

Half-truth is only partly true.

Ambiguity means more than one meaning.

Bias means favouring one thing over others.

1. our **MOST EFFECTIVE DETERGENT**

2. **The ultimate games pack**

3. HOTEL OF THE YEAR

4. FLOOD YOUR SENSES at Seatown Aquarium

5. New lower £6.99 price

6. Lightweight vacuum cleaners to make housework easier and faster.

7. **One of the most advanced all-action robotic dogs**

8. Recommended by dentists

9. FULFILS EVERY ADVENTUROUS CHILD'S DREAM

10. **WARNING you've missed 2 months' FREE online time**

11. ... admired throughout the world for its legendary strength, quality and performance

12. You too can have BEAUTIFUL HAIR

13. **MADE WITH SUN-RIPENED NATURAL GOODNESS**

14. GET A GRIP Supersafe tyres

Teachers' note Use this with page 27. Begin by discussing the terms 'half-truth', 'ambiguity', 'bias' and 'opinions disguised as facts'. Before the lesson the children could collect and bring in advertisements, and identify which of them contain any of these features. Continued on page 27.

Developing Literacy Non-fiction Year 5 © A & C Black 2002

The whole truth? 2

• **Fill in the chart.**

Advertisements using half-truths	What the full truth might be	'Half-truth' tells only part of the truth.
Advertisements using ambiguity	**The possible meanings**	'Ambiguity' means more than one meaning.
our MOST EFFECTIVE DETERGENT	1. The detergent is <u>the</u> most effective. 2. The detergent is the most effective one made by that company.	
Advertisements using bias	**How the advertisements show bias**	'Bias' means favouring one thing over others.
Advertisements giving opinions as facts	**What the real facts might be**	Opinions can be made to seem like facts.

Teachers' note Continued from page 26. You could model the first example: 'our MOST EFFECTIVE DETERGENT' is presented in a way which suggests that the detergent is 'the most effective'. It would be difficult to prove that claim and so, instead, the company words the advertisement ambiguously in a way which just suggests it; the detergent could be that manufacturer's most effective one.

Developing Literacy
Non-fiction Year 5
© A & C Black 2002

Sum it up

A |summary| **contains the main points of a text.
It leaves out the details.**
A |headline| **is a very brief summary.**

A headline doesn't need to be a sentence.

- **Read the texts.**
- **Write a summary and headline for each text. Think:**

Who?   What?   When?   Where?   Why?

Headline:	Summary
WILD boars are on the loose in the North East. One of the boars has been killed by a marksman, and forestry chiefs in Tyneside have warned that others may suffer a similar fate. Forest ranger Richard Gilchrist said that the beasts were causing problems after making their home in woods near Gateshead. He said, 'They are believed to have escaped from a farm last February.' One resident who has seen the animals said, 'Nobody knows exactly how many there are. One in particular is massive. From a distance it looks like a black Shetland pony.'	

Headline:	Summary
Police had to close the nearside lane of the A180 westbound carriageway yesterday (Friday) lunchtime after a lorry shed several bags of plaster. The incident happened shortly after 12.30 p.m. about a mile before Barnetby Top. Sergeant Brian Burns, of Scunthorpe Traffic Police, said, 'It left a coating of plaster powder on the road and created a dust cloud, which caused problems with visibility for drivers.' The outside lane remained open but traffic was slow moving. The road had been fully cleared by 3 p.m.	

Now try this!

- **Find two other newspaper articles.**
- **Write summaries of them.**

You could write your own headline for each article.

Teachers' note The questions in the speech bubbles (Who? What? When? Where? Why?) encourage the children to look for the main points of each text, although they might not be able to find answers to all of these questions. The summary should include who or what did the action, when, where and (if relevant) why. The headline should inform the reader what the text is about.

Developing Literacy
Non-fiction Year 5
© A & C Black 2002

Write a recount

- **On the flow-chart, write notes for a recount.**

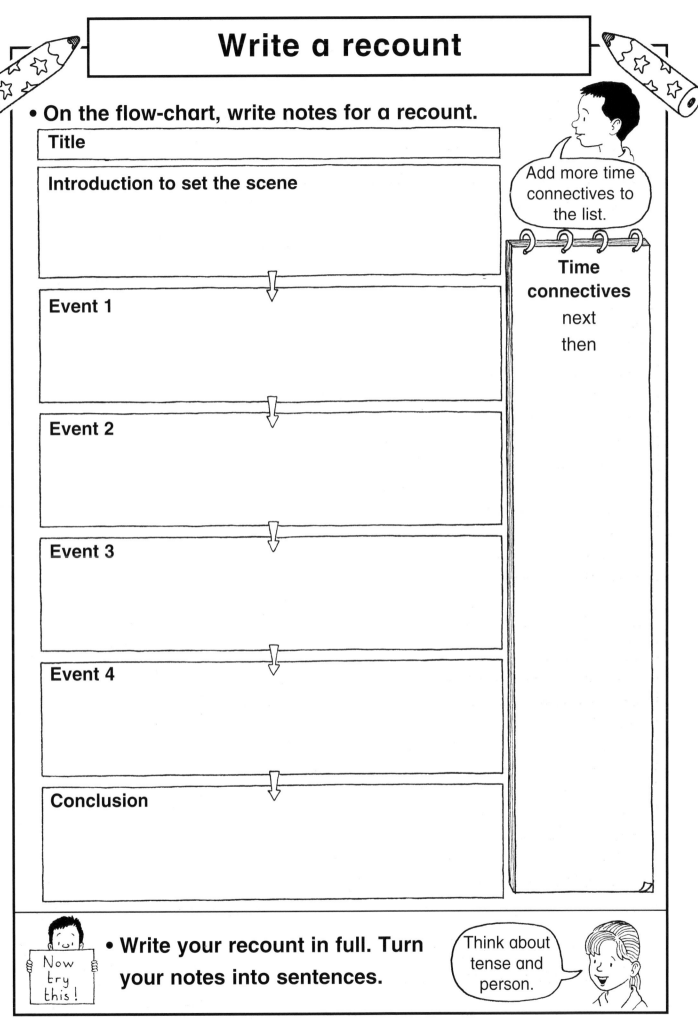

Title

Introduction to set the scene

Event 1

Event 2

Event 3

Event 4

Conclusion

Add more time connectives to the list.

Time connectives
next
then

- **Write your recount in full. Turn your notes into sentences.**

Now try this!

Think about tense and person.

Teachers' note The children should first have read and discussed recounts, such as those on pages 9 and 22. Discuss the structure of the recounts and how they are paragraphed. The children should notice the use of the past tense and 'time' connectives. The flow-chart provides a structure to help them to write in chronological order and to incorporate an introduction and a conclusion.

Developing Literacy
Non-fiction Year 5
© A & C Black 2002

Be a sports reporter

- Draft a report about the sports day using these headings.

Headline

Sub-heading

Paragraph 1 – Introduction

Paragraph 2

Paragraph 3

Paragraph 4

Paragraph 5

Paragraph 6 – Conclusion or summary

- Read the reporter's notes.

Hightown School Sports Day, Fri 10 June

Event	Place	Name	Team	Points
50 m backwards hop	1st	L Jones	Lautrec	3
	2nd	S Lee	Cézanne	2
	3rd	L Carr	Morisot	1
Custard-pie throwing	1st	A Sharma	Monet	3
	2nd	R Day	Monet	2
	3rd	L Peters	Lautrec	1
Teddy bear relay	1st	C Dove, O Agar, P Wilson, M Pye	Monet	3
	2nd	S Rowe, J Penn F Iqbal, D Wynn,	Morisot	2
	3rd	G Parr, B O'Lee, S Ng, L Grey	Lautrec	1

Final scores

Team	Points	Place
Monet	8	1st
Lautrec	5	2nd
Morisot	3	3rd
Cézanne	2	4th

Nail-biting finish to 50 m backwards hop. All set for draw: Liam Jones/Sara Lee. Liam put on spurt. Won by less than 1 sec. Bad luck for Lautrec relay team: two runners dropped teddy bear. Great run by Monet team (haven't won teddy bear relay for 4 years).

Teachers' note The children should first have read and discussed sports reports, such as the one on page 12. Revise the important features of a sports report, including the use of a headline and sub-heading to show what the sport is and the outcome, an introductory paragraph to orientate the reader, followed by paragraphs in chronological order to relate the main events, and then a summary.

Developing Literacy
Non-fiction Year 5
© A & C Black 2002

From friend to stranger

- **Read this section of a letter from Anil to his friend. He is going to write a recount of the same trip for a local magazine.**
- **Underline the parts Anil needs to change.**
- **Make notes about the changes he should make.**

Anil wrote the letter to someone he knows well. The recount is for readers he does not know.

Make the language less personal.

Notes

I'll tell you about some of the things I found out in the local study we did today.

Remember the steps we used to play on in Church Road – the ones which didn't lead anywhere? Well, the first thing we found out was that they were *always* like that. There's nothing missing; they were for people to get on to their horses at the church!

And that new house with the posh name – The King's Mill? We looked at its garden. We saw four big round blocks of stone. The owner said they were millstones from a mill which used to be there! We crossed Mill Lane to 'Cuffs' restaurant. Guess how it got its name? It used to be a police station (handcuffs!). I'd never noticed it was so old. It's made of sandstone like all the old buildings here, because there were sandstone quarries. (Remember Quarry Road?) We saw another clue above the door – an old lantern like on police stations, and the date, 1879.

- **Write Anil's recount for the magazine. Use your notes to help you.**

Now try this.

Developing Literacy
Non-fiction Year 5
© A & C Black 2002

Teachers' note The children could look for examples which show that the letter is written in personal language: for example, verbs in the first and second person; the use of the first- and second-person pronouns and omitted pronouns; informal and even colloquial vocabulary; and conversational expressions such as 'Well...'

Write a recipe

- **Look at the notes and drawings about a recipe.**
- **Write the recipe.**

Use imperative verbs. Write simple sentences.

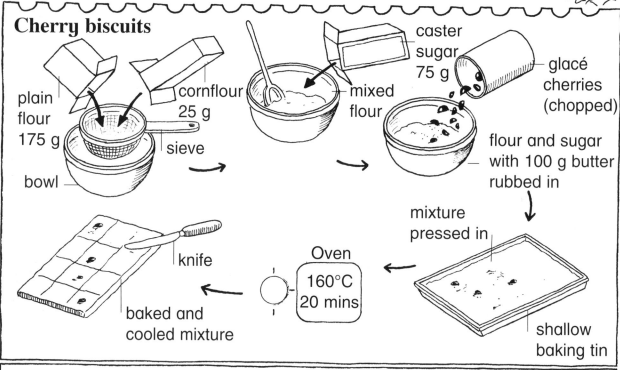

Cherry biscuits

plain flour 175 g

cornflour 25 g

sieve

bowl

mixed flour

caster sugar 75 g

glacé cherries (chopped)

flour and sugar with 100 g butter rubbed in

mixture pressed in

shallow baking tin

Oven 160°C 20 mins

knife

baked and cooled mixture

Cherry biscuits

Ingredients

_____   _____

_____

_____

Method

You could number each stage.

_____

_____

_____

_____

_____

_____

_____

_____

Teachers' note The children should first have had opportunities to read and follow recipes. They should be able to identify the key information for a recipe: the ingredients and what to do (in the correct order). Discuss any 'shorthand' in the notes which needs to be written more completely in the recipe: for example, the glacé cherries need to be chopped first.

Developing Literacy
Non-fiction Year 5
© A & C Black 2002

Scriptwriter

- **Look at the diagrams. Make an autogyro.**

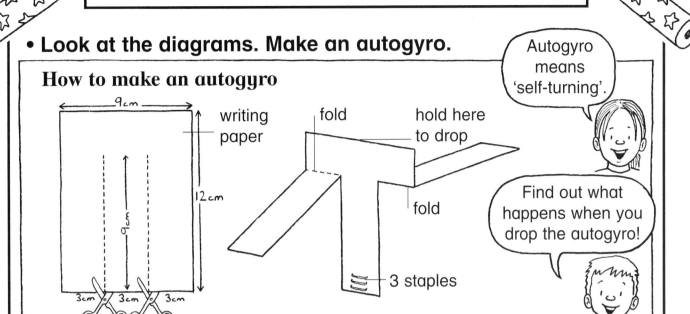

How to make an autogyro

writing paper — 9cm — 12cm — 9cm — 3cm — 3cm — 3cm

fold — hold here to drop — fold — 3 staples

Autogyro means 'self-turning'.

Find out what happens when you drop the autogyro!

- **Write a radio script. Give instructions for making and testing an autogyro.**

Say what an autogyro is and what it does.

An autogyro is _____

_____

To make it you need _____

First you need to _____

_____

_____

_____

_____

_____

_____

_____

Point out if anything needs special care.

Word-bank
finally
next
now you should have
the next step
then
this way

Now try this!

- **Read your script to someone who has not seen the diagrams. How well can he or she follow the instructions?**

Teachers' note The children first need to have read, followed and evaluated instructions (for example, those on page 10). Remind them to use imperative verbs and to write the instructions step by step in the correct order (they could number them). Point out the importance of writing simply and clearly for an audience who cannot see the pictures.

Developing Literacy Non-fiction Year 5 © A & C Black 2002

Rule writer

• **Use this page to help you write the rules for a game.**

Name of game

Include any other names for the game.

Number of players (teams or individuals)

Object of game (how to win)

Equipment, and playing area or board

How to start the game

How to play the game

Include anything that players must <u>not</u> do – and what happens if they do.

How to end the game

For example, is there a time limit?

Now try this!

• **With your group, follow someone else's instructions and play the game. Make notes about how easy it was to follow the instructions.**

Teachers' note The children could first read the rules supplied with board games, or booklets about games and sports, and identify the key features: the object of the game, the number of players, the equipment and playing area, how to start and continue the game and how to end it. There might also be penalties (as in Snakes and Ladders).

Developing Literacy Non-fiction Year 5 © A & C Black 2002

Short and sweet: 1

- **Match the abbreviations to their meanings.**
- **Glue them back to back:**

Use a dictionary.

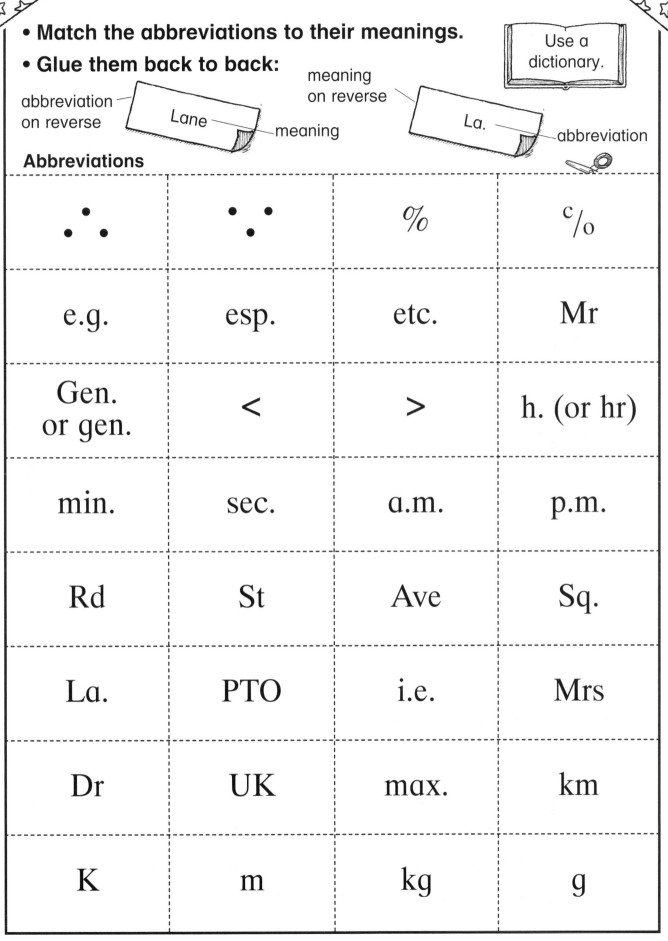

abbreviation on reverse — Lane — meaning

meaning on reverse — La. — abbreviation

Abbreviations

∴	∵	%	c/o
e.g.	esp.	etc.	Mr
Gen. or gen.	<	>	h. (or hr)
min.	sec.	a.m.	p.m.
Rd	St	Ave	Sq.
La.	PTO	i.e.	Mrs
Dr	UK	max.	km
K	m	kg	g

Teachers' note Use this with page 36. You could first show the children some of the signs, symbols and abbreviations they use in mathematics and ask them to express them in words. The children could also match road signs to their written equivalents. For ease of use, the abbreviations and meanings could be copied on to paper of different colours. Continued on page 36.

Developing Literacy
Non-fiction Year 5
© A & C Black 2002

35

Short and sweet: 2

With a friend, see how many abbreviations you know.
☆ Deal the cards (abbreviation side up) into two piles.
☆ Take turns to hold up a card so that your friend
   sees the abbreviation and you see the meaning.
☆ Score a point for every correct answer.

Meanings

afternoon (*post meridiem*)	Avenue	because	care of
Doctor	especially	etcetera (*and the rest*)	for example (*exempli gratia*)
General or generally	gram(s)	greater than or more than	hour(s)
kilogram(s)	kilometre(s)	Lane	maximum
metre(s)	minute(s) or minimum	Missus (from Mistress)	Mister
morning (*ante meridiem* = before noon)	per cent (*per centum* = for a hundred)	please turn over	Road
second(s)	smaller than or less than	Square	Street
that is (*id est*)	therefore	thousands (*khilioi*)	United Kingdom

Teachers' note Continued from page 35. You could point out the abbreviations which come from Latin and Greek words (see **Introduction** page 8). The children could make their own dictionary of useful abbreviations. Encourage them to make a note of any abbreviations they come across in books and in the environment, and to find out what they mean.

Developing Literacy Non-fiction Year 5 © A & C Black 2002

Text it

- **Read the text message.**

Use the key of text abbreviations.

> RUOK, Amy? U shld tell sum1 abt th bullyng. IK its nt UR fault, esp B/C thy'v dn it to othrs B4. W84me aftr schl 2moro. They mght call U a cwrd but thyr nt v brave B/C they only do it whn UR alon. U thnk thy'll b worse if U tll sum1, bt if U don't no1 cn hlp 2 stop thm. Hv U thght tht they mght nd hlp 2? AAMOF mny bullies need hlp.
> AISB U mst tll sum1 ASAP, B4 U get hrt. It isn't 'tllng tales'.
> HTH. B4N. Tom

Words can also be shortened by missing out the vowels.

Key	
2	to / too / two
2moro	tomorrow
AAMOF	As a matter of fact
AISB	As I said before
ASAP	As soon as possible
B/C	because
B4	before
B4N	Bye for now
esp	especially
HTH	Hope this helps
IK	I know
no1	no one
RUOK	Are you OK?
sum1	someone
U	you
UR	you are / your
W84me	Wait for me

- **Re-write the text message as a note.**

Are you OK Amy?

_____

_____

_____

_____

_____

_____

_____

_____

_____

_____

Continue on another sheet of paper.

Now try this!

- **List any other text abbreviations you know.**
- **With your group, make a larger text key.**

Teachers' note It is useful first to discuss other frequently used standard abbreviations (see pages 35–36) and contractions (for instance, can't). The children could practise keying in abbreviated text messages using a computer keyboard or mobile phone (the messages need not be sent).

Developing Literacy
Non-fiction Year 5
© A & C Black 2002

Be persuasive: 1

Use this page to plan your persuasive writing.

- In the boxes, write the main points about what you are suggesting.
- On the lines, write information to support each point. Add extra lines if you need to.

- Show your plan to a friend.
- Ask him or her to argue against your ideas.
- Add other ideas to make your plan more persuasive.

Teachers' note The children should first have read and discussed examples of persuasive texts (for example, the one on page 23), before choosing a topic to write about. The format provided here for the writing of a persuasive text has a similar structure to that on page 23, for making notes. In the extension activity, partners could make notes of their responses, for discussion during the plenary session.

Developing Literacy
Non-fiction Year 5
© A & C Black 2002

Be persuasive: 2

• **Use persuasive language to link your ideas.**

Heading _____

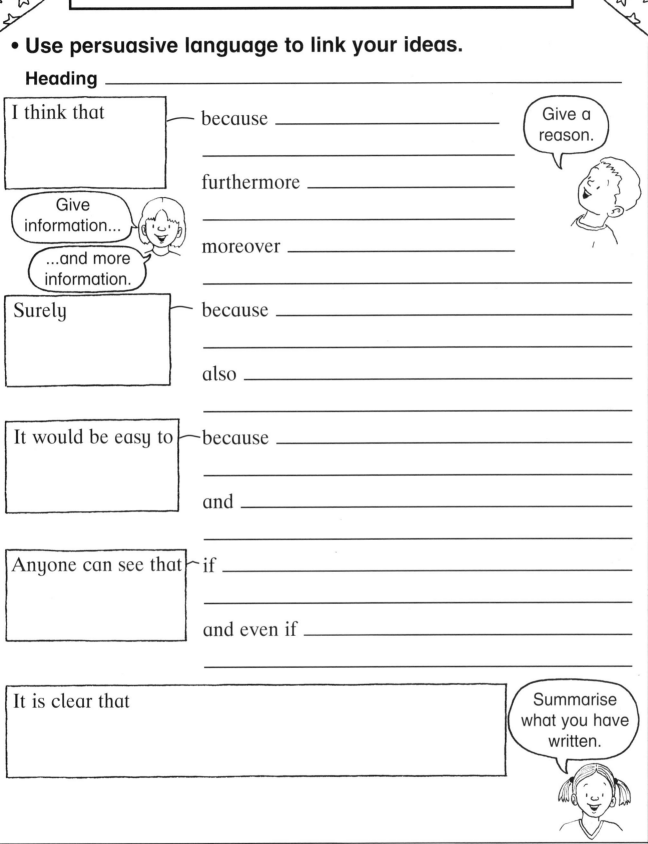

I think that

because _____

_____

furthermore _____

_____

moreover _____

Give a reason.

Give information...

...and more information.

Surely

because _____

_____

also _____

It would be easy to

because _____

_____

and _____

_____

Anyone can see that

if _____

_____

and even if _____

_____

It is clear that

Summarise what you have written.

• **Write your persuasive text as a letter to a newspaper.**

Teachers' note The children should first complete the activity on page 38, where the emphasis is on the structure of a persuasive text, and have that page available for reference. In this activity there is more emphasis on persuasive language and the use of connectives to link the ideas.

**Developing Literacy
Non-fiction Year 5
© A & C Black 2002**

Five steps for taking notes

Teachers' note The children can use this page to evaluate the way in which they take notes. They should focus on a single question to research and write a summary of what they did in the boxes. During the plenary session, you could discuss what they have learned about note-taking and help them to identify one aspect of their method on which they can work for improvement.

Developing Literacy
Non-fiction Year 5
© A & C Black 2002

Calendar notes

• **Read Contrary Mary's notes. Complete the gardening calendar.**

Use a dictionary.

Dig trenches for silver bells Jan, & dig in bone meal. Dig over again Feb, & put up canes/other supports. Sweet pea seedlings – plant Mar. Add mulch May. Fasten stems to supports June, cont. July. Pinch out tendrils and side shoots.

Dig over beds for new pretty maids Feb, plant May. Prune cockle shells Mar/Apr. Feed, spray against green-fly Apr. Mulch with grass cuttings & manure end Apr. Continue to spray against greenfly (also remove diseased leaves & dead flowers) May – Sept.

Re-seed worn parts of lawn & spread lawn feed Mar. Aerate by spiking with fork Apr. Mow regularly Apr – Oct. Weed regularly Apr – Sept. Jun – Sept water lawn in dry weather and spike to let water into soil. Feed Oct. One final mowing Nov. Dig over any bare patches Dec.

Contrary Mary's gardening calendar

January	February	March
Dig trenches		
April	May	June
July	August	September
October	November	December

Now try this!

• **Make an enlarged copy of the calendar.**
• **Add other gardening tasks.**

Use information books.

Teachers' note You could begin by discussing how a gardening calendar might be easier for a gardener to use than the notes. Point out that the notes were intended only for the gardener's own use, but that once they have been organised in the form of a calendar, other people can follow them more easily. Revise abbreviations as used in the notes if necessary.

Developing Literacy
Non-fiction Year 5
© A & C Black 2002

Family tree notes

- **Read the extracts from** *Egil's Saga*.
- **Find the information you need to complete the family tree.**

There was a man named Ulf (called Kveld-Ulf), the son of Bjalfi and of Hallbera. He became a Viking and went raiding. His partner was a man named Kari. Kveld-Ulf married Kari's daughter Salbjorg and settled down to live on his farm.

Kveld-Ulf and Salbjorg had two sons; the elder was named Thorolf and the younger was named Grim (people called him Skallagrim). Skallagrim married Bera, the daughter of Yngvar of Fjordane. Skallagrim and Bera had a son named Thorolf, then two daughters named Sœunn and Thorunn and another son named Egil. Egil married Asgerd, the daughter of Bjorn Brynjolfsson and Thora Lace-Sleeve. They had two daughters named Thorgerd and Bera and three sons named Bodvar, Gunnar and Thorstein.

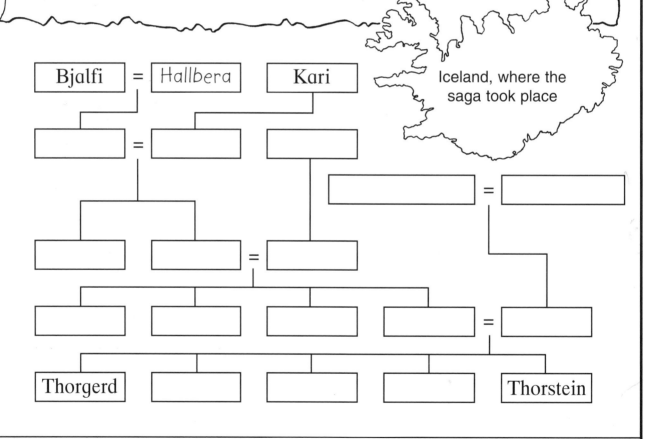

| Bjalfi | = | Hallbera | Kari |

Iceland, where the saga took place

Thorgerd | | | | Thorstein

Now try this!

- **Write about the people in another family. Draw the family tree.**

You could write about a royal family.

Teachers' note You could begin by inviting a child to come to the front and tell the class about his or her family tree. Then ask the class questions about the family tree, for example: 'Who is the husband of Kelly's mother's sister?' Help the child to fill in a family tree on a large sheet of paper, and then ask more questions about it. The children should notice that the family tree makes this task easier.

**Developing Literacy
Non-fiction Year 5
© A & C Black 2002**

Notes to text

- **Read the notes about the Ancient Greeks.**
- **Re-write them in sentences.**

The headings help you to split the text into paragraphs.

Homes

Walls made of mud-baked bricks, sometimes plastered. Small windows high up (no glass, wooden shutters). Roof made of clay tiles. In main room hearth for cooking (brick w. portable metal container for charcoal to burn). Altar for sacrifices ➤ gods.

Clothes

Men + women wore chiton (2 ☐s). Pinned at shldrs & fastened at intervals down sides to make sleeves. Long (neck ➤ feet). Tied at waist by sash. Children: shorter chiton/tunic to knee. Cloak if cold. Hat ➤ keep off sun (wool, straw, fur). Rich had coloured (dyed) clothes; poor – plain.

Food

Fruits: grapes, oranges, figs. Olives. Olive oil. Fish & seafood: mackerel, squid. Made bread, cakes & bisc. (honey ➤ sweeten). Kept goats for milk & cheese; hens for eggs. Drank wine mixed w. water. Meat not often for poor (spec. occasions). Rich ate wild deer, boar, hares.

Ancient Greek homes were built from sun-baked mud bricks.

_____

_____

_____

_____

_____

_____

_____

_____

Continue on another sheet of paper.

- **Read through what you have written. Mark any parts which you can improve. Re-draft your work.**

Teachers' note Before beginning, discuss the way in which the notes are written. Point out the abbreviations and symbols and ask the children if they know what they all represent; ask them to supply any missing words and explain why they have been missed out.

**Developing Literacy
Non-fiction Year 5
© A & C Black 2002**

From notes to report

- **Read Jo's notes about a castle's instruments of torture.**

For making victim confess or give info	For 'trial' or test of victim	For punishment of victim
<u>Thumbscrews</u>: tightened <u>The rack</u>: victim stretched using ropes	<u>Sack</u>: woman accused of witchcraft put in sack and thrown into moat. If sank - 'innocent'; if floated - 'guilty'	<u>Ducking stool</u>: victim tied to it and ducked in river

- **Write a** non-chronological report **about the instruments of torture.**

Write sentences. Use present tense verbs. Think about active and passive verbs.

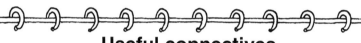
Useful connectives

also	in order to	the first
another	so that	the outcome
for example	that	the second

The castle dungeons contain a collection of _____ _____

> Write an introductory sentence.

These had three main purposes: _____

_____

_____

> Introduce the collection of instruments of torture.

_____

_____

_____

> Describe the instruments of torture.

_____

_____

Teachers' note You could begin by discussing the ways in which notes differ from a finished report: they are not written in complete sentences, and abbreviations, signs and symbols are used to replace words. The writer of the notes on this page has organised the notes to suit her purpose, by grouping the information according to the uses of the instruments of torture.

Developing Literacy Non-fiction Year 5 © A & C Black 2002

Change the audience

- **Read the text.**
- **Re-write it for a child in Year 1.**

Use simple words.

Write short, simple sentences.

Explain any words which might be new to the reader.

Change passive verbs to active.

Text	Change to
Because plants cannot escape from animals which eat them, some plants have developed special ways of avoiding being eaten.	Many animals eat plants. Some plants have ways to stop them.
Others, like grass, simply carry on growing when their leaves, stems and flowers have been eaten.	
To keep small insects away, some plants have developed a covering of tiny hairs on the surface of their leaves.	
Other plants, such as cacti, roses and nettles, deter larger animals by means of spines, thorns and stings.	
The leaves of some plants – for example, holly – are so tough and leathery that they are rarely eaten by animals. Holly is further protected by the spines on its leaves.	

Now try this!

- **Discuss your ideas with a friend.**
- **Edit your new text using a different-coloured pen.**
- **Re-draft and illustrate it for a child in Year 1.**

Teachers' note The children should first compare books written for children in Year 1 with those written for older children, and look for the features that characterise them. Encourage them to discuss each section of the text and to decide what information it gives and how that information can be written more simply.

Developing Literacy
Non-fiction Year 5
© A & C Black 2002

Make it formal

- **Write each extract in a more formal way.**

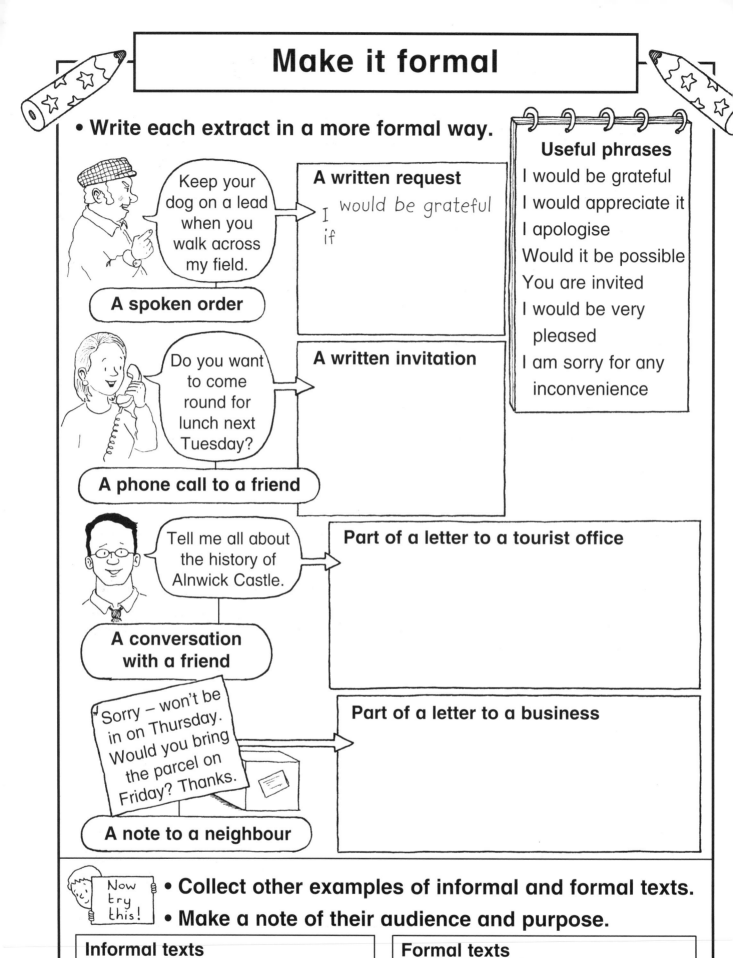

Keep your dog on a lead when you walk across my field.

A spoken order

A written request

I *would be grateful* if

Do you want to come round for lunch next Tuesday?

A phone call to a friend

A written invitation

Useful phrases

I would be grateful
I would appreciate it
I apologise
Would it be possible
You are invited
I would be very pleased
I am sorry for any inconvenience

Tell me all about the history of Alnwick Castle.

A conversation with a friend

Part of a letter to a tourist office

Sorry – won't be in on Thursday. Would you bring the parcel on Friday? Thanks.

A note to a neighbour

Part of a letter to a business

Now try this!

- **Collect other examples of informal and formal texts.**
- **Make a note of their audience and purpose.**

Informal texts		
Text	Audience	Purpose

Formal texts		
Text	Audience	Purpose

Teachers' note The children will find this easier if they first complete the activity on page 11, in which they develop skills in identifying the features of formal and informal language.

Developing Literacy Non-fiction Year 5 © A & C Black 2002

Write a commentary

• **Use this page to plan a** commentary .

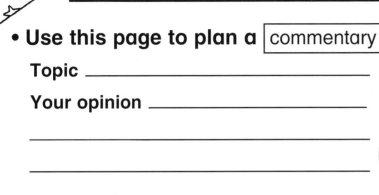
In a commentary you can give your opinion of, say, a film, a book or an issue.

Topic _____

Your opinion _____

_____

_____

A commentary should help the reader to understand the subject.

Key points to support your opinion

• _____
_____

• _____
_____

• _____
_____

• _____
_____

Information that you need to check	Where you will check it	What you found out

Check to make sure the points you make are correct.

Summary _____

_____

_____

Use logical connectives.

Now try this!

• **Write or key in your commentary.**
• **Edit and re-draft it.**

Teachers' note It is useful to revise the differences between an argument and a commentary: an argument considers an issue from different points of view, albeit favouring one of them, supporting it with evidence and countering any opposing views, whereas a commentary sets out to present one point of view, supported by evidence, but does not attempt to persuade the reader.

Developing Literacy
Non-fiction Year 5
© A & C Black 2002

Present an argument

Write in note form.

Topic

Your opinion

Points supporting your opinion	Points against your opinion	How you will argue against them

Summary

- **Write your argument so that you can present it as a talk.**
- **To help you remember it, write on separate cards:**

  the topic and your opinion

  each point supporting your opinion

  each point against your opinion (and your answer to it)

  your summary

You need cards the size of postcards.

- **Practise your argument with a friend. Your friend could argue against the points you make.**

Teachers' note The children should first have read and discussed examples of arguments. You could begin by giving the children an issue to consider. Note that when presenting an argument as a talk they need only present the points in favour of their opinion, and keep those against it in case anyone challenges them at the end of their talk.

Developing Literacy Non-fiction Year 5 © A & C Black 2002